JOHANNES BRAHMS

SEXTET

for 2 Violins, 2 Violas and 2 Violoncellos
B♭ major/B-Dur/Si♭ majeur
Op. 18

Edited by/Herausgegeben von
Wilhelm Altmann

Ernst Eulenburg Ltd
London · Mainz · Madrid · New York · Paris · Prague · Tokyo · Toronto · Zürich

CONTENTS

Ernst Eulenburg Ltd
48 Great Marlborough Street
London W1F 7BB

PREFACE

Although Spohr, as early as 1850, composed as his op. 140 a Sextet for 2 Violins, 2 Violas and 2 Violoncellos, it fell really to Brahms to inaugurate this form of musical literature by his two fine Sextets op. 18 and 36. It is hardly likely that Brahms was influenced by Spohr's work. We learn for the first time that he was employed upon a Sextet from a letter written to Brahms by Joachim (presumably March 26th 1860), asking the composer to have the parts of the Sextet copied out. On Apr. 29th Joachim asks: –"How is the Sextet getting on?" and adds: –"This is the time for it". But the work was not sent to the great violinist until September. In an accompanying letter Brahms wrote: –"I have been rather long over it and I do not suppose that will have raised your expectations. But, as the Lord makes all things possible, in case you should care for the Rondo I am sending you the parts. If you have no scruples about the work, and like it, please ask Deierberg to copy the work at my expense. I should very much like to be invited to a rehearsal very soon. But send the composition back if it fails to please you." Joachim replied on Oct. 8th: –"I have just given your Sextet to the copyist and hope to run through it next Sunday morning. I am much pleased with the general conception and execution of the new movement. The finish is successful, light and lively in mood. You are to be congratulated on having completed another artistic work. I hope to play it at our second Soirée, next Saturday week." Joachim wrote to his friend again on Oct. 14th as follows: –"We have played over your Sextet twice and want to try it publicly next Saturday evening. It pleases me very much, especially the first two movements. The Scherzo is full of life and I like the Finale, but I expected a little more force at the end and wish the second subject had more contrast to the first. But the performance was faulty. The last movement is the hardest. The second rehearsal is fixed for early next Wednesday and after that we shall have another one. Come to the performance; Madame Schumann will be there." Brahms accepted at once, adding: –"I should never have thought everything would have gone so smoothly and was rather nervous about the long sentimental movement."

Madame Schumann wrote in her diary after the first performance of the Sextet. – "It was far beyond my expectations, which were already high." She already knew the second movement, the Variations in D which Brahms may have sent her in the original Piano form: on Sep. 16th she thanked Brahms that she was at last able to play these Variations for herself. Unfortunately they are as yet unpublished in this form. Florence May, the master's pupil and biographer states that the very first composition he played to her in 1871 were these same Variations and that he seemed to delight in them.

When Brahms left Hannover he did not take the Sextet with him. Joachim wrote to him on Nov. 23nd: –"Don't be angry because I am still keeping your work! I want to take it to Leipzig and play it there on Sunday or Tuesday, at David's house or Härtel's. After that I will return it. It has not been neglected here, for last

Sunday evening we played it privately, as I had arranged some music for the Ambassador in Vienna, von Stockhausen. It gave us all a lot of pleasure and went well with the same players as before."

Clara Schumann's diary testifies that the performance in Leipzig on Nov. 27th took place at the Conservatoire, before an audience, and had enormous success. Brahms was present; he had conducted his Serenade op. 16 there some days before but this wonderfully poetic work had been but coldly received. The Sextet, however, soon made a stir in other places, especially in Hamburg, but, strange to say, fell flat at the first performance in Vienna, led by Hellmesberger in the Autumn of 1862.

In July 1861 Brahms sent the work to the publisher Simrock in Bonn asking 16 Friedrichdors for it, including the 4 handed Piano arrangement, and modestly begging Simrock to print the score as well, which was not usual at the time. As old Peter Joseph Simrock was not satisfied with the sales of the Serenade op. 16 he came near to losing the Sextet, which proved later to be in such great demand. It required all the persuasion of his son Fritz, who was a devotee of Brahms's music, and had journeyed from Berlin for the purpose to induce the old man to take the Sextet and print the score as well. In Sep. 1861 Brahms wrote to Joachim: –"Some time ago I sent my Sextet fearfully and unwillingly to Simrock. I have an unpleasant idea that it is not all it should be, and that I should have sent it to you again first." A few days later he wrote again: –"I cannot help sending you the corrections. If you have any doubts let me have a line. I specially want you to see to the bowing and phrasing. I am always rather chary of marking these so as not to annoy the player. Some of the fingering is unnecessary, in other places it is wanting. Underline anything you think is good… "On Oct. 3rd Brahms wrote again: –"You will have seen to your sorrow that the Sextet is published. It is true it might have turned out better had I waited a little longer, but waiting has its bad side." Joachim replied on Oct. 15th: –"Your work travelled to Simrock the day after its arrival, duly fingered and bowed. The Piano arrangement is very playable and sounds well. The work gave me the same pleasure as before. I would not have it different and am glad it is alive, and J. J. as well, to play it often." During his long artistic career Joachim lived to play it more than merely often.

Wilhelm Altmann

VORWORT

Wenn auch Spohr bereits im Jahre 1850 als sein 140. Werk zuerst ein Sextett für 2 Violinen, 2 Bratschen und 2 Violoncelle veröffentlicht hat, so ist diese Gattung von Kammermusikwerken eigentlich erst durch die beiden herrlichen Sextette von Brahms Op. 18 und 36 der musikalischen Literatur gewonnen worden. Dass er durch jenes Spohrsche Werk angeregt worden ist, ist kaum anzunehmen. Dass er an einem Sextett gearbeitet hat, erfahren wir zuerst aus einem wahrscheinlich am 26. März 1860 geschriebenen Briefe Joachims, worin dieser den Freund auffordert, die Stimmen vom Sextett ausschreiben zu lassen. Am 29. April frägt dann Joachim: „Wie ist's mit dem Sextett?" und fügt hinzu: „Wir hätten jetzt schöne Zeit dazu". Aber erst im September erhielt er das fertige Sextett. In dem Begleitbriefe dazu schrieb Brahms: „Es dauert manchmal etwas lange bei mir; das wird wohl Deine Erwartungen nicht höher treiben. Da nun bei Gott kein Ding unmöglich ist, so lege ich für den Fall, daß Dir das Rondo zusagen sollte, die Stimmen bei. Hast Du keine besonderen Bedenken und Lust dazu, so lasse Deierberg die Stimmen auf meine Rechnung fertig schreiben. Ich möchte wohl, ich würde recht bald zu einer Probe eingeladen. Doch schicke es ja zurück, falls Dir das Stück nicht zusagt." Joachim erwiderte hierauf am 8. Oktober: „Eben habe ich Dein Sextett zum Kopisten gebracht und denke, es am nächsten Sonntagvormittag bei mir zu hören. Der neue Satz gefällt mir in Stimmung und Aufführung gar sehr. Schon das Motiv nimmt durch Anmut und Wärme ein, und das ganze fließt edel und wohltuend auf der Höhe der ersten Empfindung hin. Glücklich ist auch der Schluß, leicht und lebendig gesteigert. So darf man Dir denn wieder einmal zur Vollendung eines Kunstwerkes gratulieren, das seines Meisters Lob singt! Ich hoffe es in unserer zweiten Soiree, nächsten Sonnabend über acht Tage, zu bringen". Als Ergänzung hierzu schrieb Joachim dem Freunde bereits am 14. Oktober: „Wir haben Dein Sextett zweimal durchgespielt und wollen's am nächsten Samstag abend öffentlich spielen. Es hat mir ganz ausnehmend gefallen, zumal die beiden ersten Sätze. Auch das Scherzo ist sehr lebendig, und ich liebe auch das Finale; nur hatt' ich mir vom Schluß mehr Wirkung versprochen und wünschte das zweite Thema wohl etwas kontrastierender mit dem ersten, dem es an Lieblichkeit nicht gleichkommt. Doch lag auch in der Ausführung mit Schuld; der letzte ist der schwerste Satz. Wir halten Mittwoch früh die zweite Probe und dann noch eine. Komme zur Aufführung... Auch Frau Schumann kommt..." Brahms sagte sofort sein Erscheinen zu und tat dabei die Äußerung: „Ich dachte nicht, daß alles so fix ginge, und hatte Angst vor dem langen sentimentalen Stück".

Nach der Uraufführung schrieb Frau Schumann in ihr Tagebuch über dieses Sextett: „Es war über meine Erwartung schön, und diese war schon bedeutend genug gewesen". Sie kannte übrigens schon den zweiten Satz, die Variationen in d, die Brahms ihr in der vielleicht ursprünglichen Klavier-Fassung zugesandt hatte; am 16. September hatte sie sich bei Brahms dafür bedankt, dass sie endlich diese Variationen sich selbst spielen könne. Sie sind leider in der Klavierform bis heute ungedruckt geblieben. Florence May, die Schülerin und Biographin des Meisters, behauptet, die erste seiner Kompositionen, die er ihr 1871 vorgespielt habe, seien diese Variationen gewesen; er soll sie überhaupt sehr gern, wenn er dem Spielen sich nicht entziehen konnte, vorgetragen haben.

Als er nach der Uraufführung des Sextetts von Hannover abreiste, gab es ihm Joachim noch nicht mit. Dieser schrieb ihm am 23. November: „Sei mir nicht böse, daß Du Dein Sextett noch immer nicht hast. Ich will es nur noch nach Leipzig mitnehmen, wo ich es Sonntag oder Dienstag irgendwo, etwa bei David oder Härtels, spielen mochte. Dann bekommst Du es zurück. Es hat bei mir nicht brach gelegen; noch Sonntag abend führten wir es bei mir privatim auf, da ich für den Hannoverschen Gesandten in Wien Ex. v. Stockhausen etwas Musik arrangiert habe. Es hat wieder uns allen die größte Freude gemacht und ging noch recht gut in der alten Besetzung“.

Dass diese Leipziger Aufführung am 27. November im dortigen Konservatorium (wohl vor einem geladenen Publikum) stattgefunden und gezündet hat, wissen wir aus Clara Schumanns Tagebuch. Brahms war dabei auch anwesend; tags zuvor hatte er seine Serenade Op. 16 im Gewandhauskonzerte selbst dirigiert, dieses wundervoll poetische Werk war aber leider kalt aufgenommen worden. Das Sextett hatte aber sehr bald auch an anderen Orten, vor allem in Hamburg, großen Erfolg, der merkwürdigerweise bei der ersten Wiener Aufführung durch Hellmesberger im Herbst 1862 ausblieb.

Im Juli 1861 schickte es Brahms nach Bonn an den Verlag Simrock und verlangte dafür einschließlich des Auszugs für Klavier zu 4 Händen 16 Friedrichsdor, bat auch sehr bescheidentlich um den damals ungewöhnlichen Druck der Partitur. Da der alte Peter Joseph Simrock von dem geschäftlichen Erfolge der Serenade Op. 16 bisher wenig erfreut war, hätte er beinahe dieses Sextett, welches eines der gangbarsten Werke werden sollte, sich entgehen lassen. Es bedurfte sehr des Zuredens seines von der Brahmsschen Musik begeisterten Sohnes Fritz, der von Berlin extra dazu herübergereist war, um ihn zu der Verlagsübernahme zu bestimmen; er ließ dann aber auch gleich sogar die Partitur stechen. Der Komponist schrieb übrigens im September 1861 an Joachim: „Mein Sextett habe ich mit Unlust und Herzklopfen vor längerem an Simrock geschickt. Auch jetzt ist mir der unangenehmste Gedanke, es nicht, wie ich wollte, vorher noch Dir geschickt zu haben. Ich dächte, Du sähest Dir meine Sachen zuwider. Hättest Du was zu erinnern? Bei der Revision wäre es Zeit“. Einige Tage später schrieb Brahms wieder an Joachim: „Ich kann's, nicht lassen, Dir die Korrektur des Sextetts zu schicken... Hättest Du besondere Bedenken, so schreibe doch eine Zeile deshalb. Vor allem möchte ich, daß Du die Bogen, Bindungen etwas korrigierst. Ich bin aus Bescheidenheit, um die Violinspieler nicht zu genieren, etwas unordentlich damit. Auch stehen wohl unnütze Finger hier und fehlen anderwo welche. Streiche natürlich alles an, was Dir gut scheint...“ Am 3. Oktober schrieb er dann nochmals an den Freund: „Mein Sextett wirst Du wohl mit einigem Seufzen schon gedruckt gesehen haben. Es ist wahr, wenn ich noch gewartet hätte, es hätte vielleicht besser werden können, aber das Warten hat auch sein Übles.“ Joachim erwiderte am 15. Oktober: „Dein Sextett ist gleich den Tag nach seiner Ankunft zu Simrock gewandert, befingert und bestrichartet. Den Klavierauszug habe sogar ich (den Baß natürlich) ziemlich fließend herauskriegen können (mit Bernhard Scholz, der auch sehr lobte). Du arrangierst köstlich spielbar und wohlklingend. Es hat mir wieder rechten Genuß gewährt, das gemütvolle, reiche Stück! Ich wüßte nichts anders zu wünschen und freue mich, daß es auf der Welt ist, und J. J. auch, um es manchmal zu spielen". Letzteres hat ja Joachim während seiner langen Künstlertätigkeit sehr viel mehr als nur manchmal getan.

Wilhelm Altmann

SEXTET

I

Johannes Brahms
(1833–1897)
Op. 18

20
poco f
cresc.
cresc.
cresc.
cresc.
cresc.
cresc.

30
f
p
40
pcresc.
cresc.
tranquillo
p dolce
p
dolce

50
p dolce
p
dolce
60
poco rit.
in tempo
pp dolce
pp dolce
pp dolce
pizz.
arco
pp dolce
pizz.
arco
pp

70
pp
pizz.
arco
80
cresc.
poco f espress. animato
p

90
espress. animato
poco f
f espress.
poco f
cresc.
cresc.
cresc.
cresc.
poco f
cresc.
100

fp
p
p dolce
pizz.
f
arco
110
pp
poco a poco cresc.
120

mf cresc.
arco
pizz.
130
f
p dim.
dim.
pp
pp dim.
p
pizz
arco
140

arco
p espress.
pizz.
p
p espress.
pizz.
p
p
150
rf
rf
arco
poco più f
mf
pizz.
mf
poco più f
arco
poco più f espress.
160
arco

170
cresc.
f
arco
marcato
pizz.
180

ff
190
fp
p

pizz.
200
arco
p
espress.
espress.
210

p
arco
p
220
p poco a poco cresc.
p poco a poco cresc.
p poco a poco cresc.
p poco a poco cresc.
p poco a poco cresc.
p poco a poco cresc.
230
cresc.
cresc.
cresc.
cresc.
cresc.
cresc.

più f sempre cresc.
più f sempre cresc.
più f sempre cresc.
più f sempre cresc.
più f sempre crec.
più f sempre cresc.
240
ff
ff
sf
sf
sf

250
ff
fz
260
f
p

270
p dolce calmato
p dolce
p
espress.
280
p dolce
dolce
p
espress.
dolce
poco rit.
dim.
dim.
dim.

in tempo
290
pp dolce
pp dolce
pp
pp dolce
pp dolce
pizz.
p
arco
p
300
pizz.
p
arco
pizz.
arco
cresc.
cresc.
cresc.
cresc.
cresc.
cresc.

310
p
poco f espress. animato
p
p
cresc.
cresc.
cresc.
cresc.
320
f espress. animato
poco f
poco f
f espress.
cresc.
cresc.
cresc.
cresc.
cresc.

330
fp
p dolce
pizz.
f
p
arco
340

p
pp
pp
pp
pp
pp
pizz.
pizz.
poco a poco cresc.
poco a poco cresc.
poco a poco cresc.
poco a poco cresc.
350
mf cresc.
arco
mf cresc.
mf cresc.
cresc.
pizz.
cresc.
mf cresc.
f
f
p dim.
p dim.
p dim.
p dim.

360
p dim.
pp
pp dim.
pizz.
arco
p espress.
p
870
cresc.
molto espress.
f cresc.
arco
f espress.
mf
f

380
dim. e rit.
Poco più Moderato
pizz.
p
390
arco
f
pp

II

Andante, ma Moderato

30
40

f
f
f
f
50
f
f
f
f
f
p dolce
p dolce
p dolce
p dolce
p

cresc.
cresc.
tr
tr
60
molto cresc.
molto cresc.
f (2a. ♩)
f (2a. ♩)

p f

più f
f più f
f più f
più f
f più f
ff
80
ff
f molto espressivo
f molto espress.
f
f molto espressivo
f molto espressivo
f molto espressivo
f

90
molto espress.
3
3
100
f
f
110
molto espress.
cresc.
cresc.
cresc.
cresc.
cresc.
cresc.

pp dolce
Solo pp dolce
p
2a. pp
(1a.)
120
p
rf
rf
pizz.
mf
pizz.
p
mf
p
mf
mf
p

pp
1.
2.
arco
p
130 pizz.
pizz.
arco
140
f

arco
p
arco
p
p
p
p
p
150
p
p
dim.
dim.
dim.
dim.
dim.
dim.

III. Scherzo

Allegro molto
Violino I
Violino II
Viola I
Viola II
Violoncello I
Violoncello II
tr
mf
pizz.
cresc.
10
f
arco

20
fp
pizz.
tr
30
cresc.
più cresc.

40
arco
arco
Trio
Animato
tr
tr
50
ff
ffz
ff sempre

60
tr
70
ff
80
1.
2.
Scherzo da capo senza replica
sin al 𝄋 e poi il Coda

Coda
Più animato
tr
ff
ffz
sempre più f
90
100
8

IV. Rondo

Poco Allegretto e grazioso
Violino I
Violino II
Viola I
Viola II
Violoncello I
Violoncello II
p
espressivo
pizz.
tr
10
20
espress.
legato
plegato
sempre leg.

30
tr
p
p dolce
arco
espress.
40
poco f
pizz.

50
cresc.
cresc.
cresc.
cresc.
cresc.
cresc.
arco
f
arco
f
60
p
p dolce
p dolce
p dolce
pizz.
p
pizz.
arco
sf
p
areo

70
f
p
p espress.
pp
80
90

100
p espress.
110

120
p
f
dolce
p dolce
pdolce
130
pp
140
poco f
pizz.

150
tr
pdolce
arco
espress.
160
cresc
cresc.
arco
poco f

170
tr
cresc.
pizz.
180
p
f
arco

190
f espress.
f espress.
200
f espress.
f espress.
210

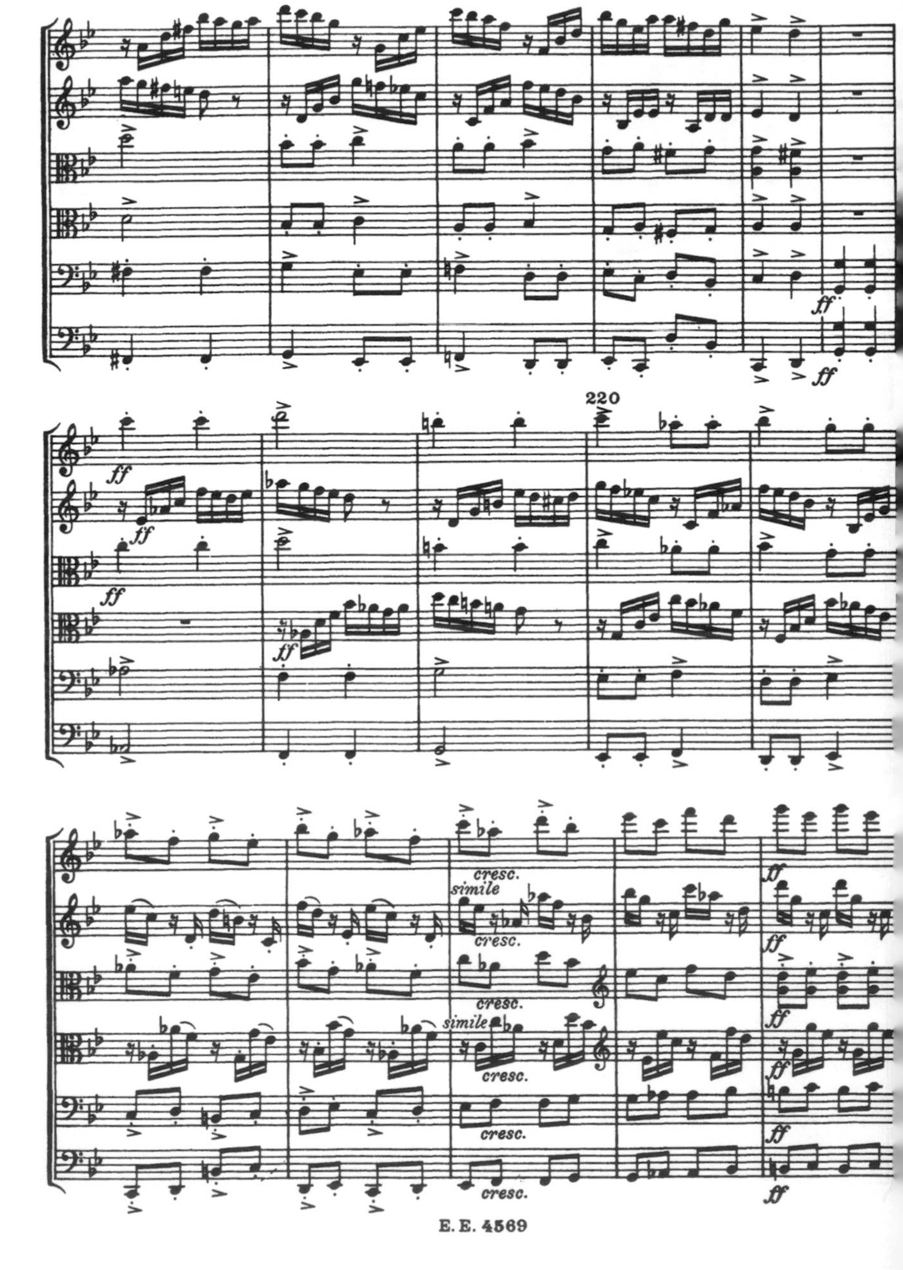

ff
220
cresc.
simile

230
ff
p dolce
p dolce
dim.
p stacc.
dim.
p stacc.
pizz.
240
p
p
p
p
p
p

250
pp
pp
pp
pp
pp
pp
cresc.
cresc.
cresc.
cresc.
arco
260
ff
ff
ff
ff
ff
ff
ff

ff
p
270
dim.
280
dolce

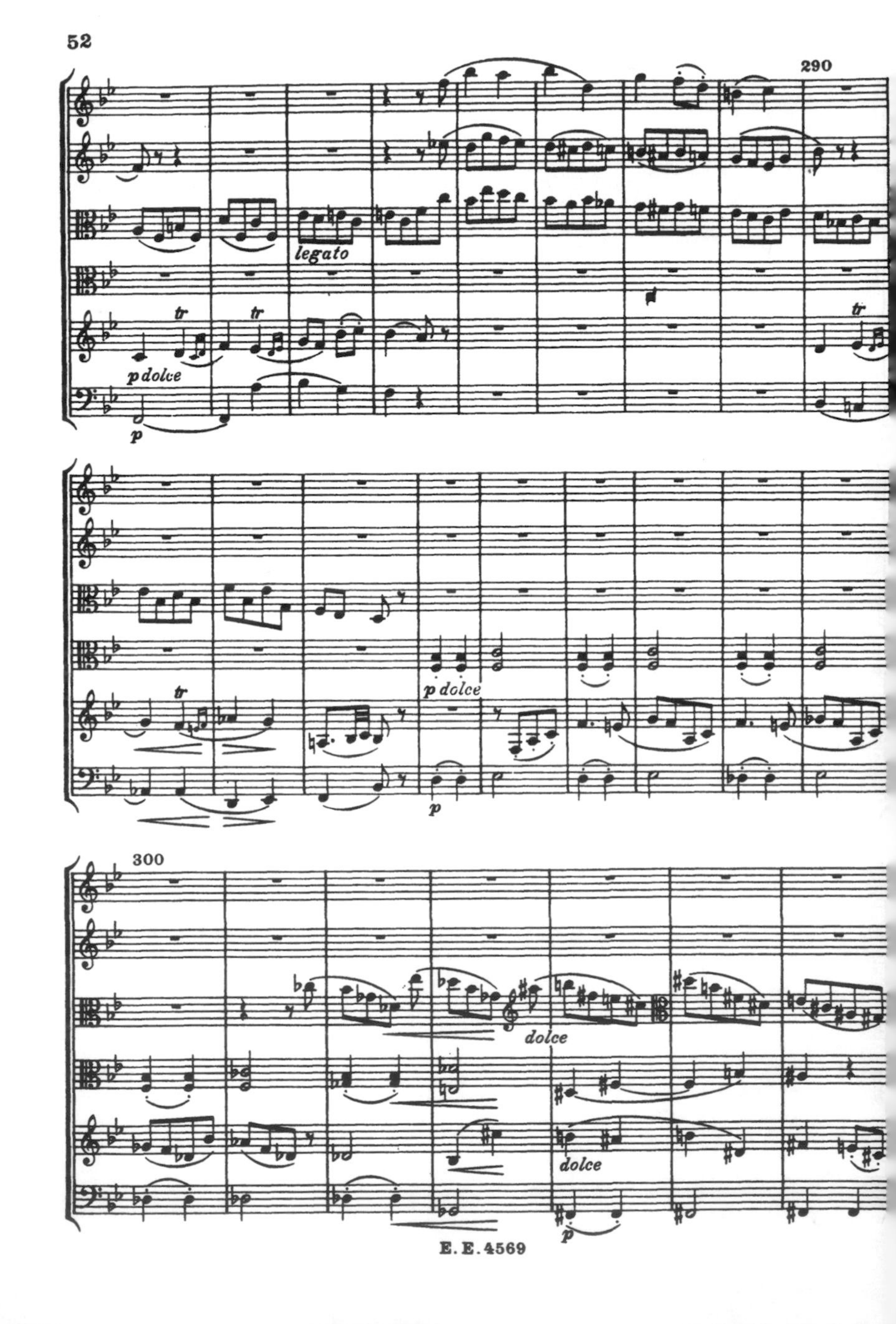
290
legato
tr
p dolce
p
300
dolce
p

310
tr
cresc.
320
p
p dolce
pp dolce

330
340
350
p espress.

360
370
dolce
p dolce
pp

380
p
pp
pp
p
p
p
p
dim.
dim.
dim.
390
pp dolce
pp dolce
pp dolce
pp
dolce
pp dolce
pp
dolce
400

p dolce
p dolce
p
pizz.
espress.
p
410
cresc.
cresc.
cresc.
cresc.
cresc.
f
f
f
f
f
poco f
pizz.
pizz. poco f
poco f
poco f
poco f
tr
tr
420

arco
espress.
cresc.
cresc.
cresc.
cresc.
cresc.
cresc.
f
430
arco
f
f espress.
f
f
arco
f
più f molto espress.
più f molto espress.
più f
più f
più f
più f

440
dim.
dim.
dim.
dim.
dim.
dim.
p
p
p
p
450
pizz.
p
pizz.
p
pizz.
p
pizz.
p
pespress.
pespress.
460
pizz.
pizz.
arco
p
arco
p
arco
p
arco
p

Animato, poco a poco più
470
poco marc.
poco marc.
p leggiero
pizz.
p poco marc.
pizz.
p poco marc.

480
arco
p
arco
p
p legg.
pizz.
p
arco
p
arco
p
490
cresc.
cresc.
cresc.
arco
p cresc.
cresc.
cresc.

f
500
ff